ARKANSAS
TOTAL ECLIPSE GUIDE

Official Commemorative
2024 Keepsake Guidebook

2024 Total Eclipse State Guide Series

Aaron Linsdau

SASTRUGI PRESS

JACKSON HOLE

Sastrugi Press / Published by arrangement with the author

Arkansas Total Eclipse Guide: Official Commemorative 2024 Keepsake Guidebook

The author has made every effort to accurately describe the locations contained in this work. Travel to some locations in this book is hazardous. The publisher has no control over and does not assume any responsibility for author or third-party websites or their content describing these locations, how to travel there, nor how to do it safely. Refer to local regulations and laws.

Any person exploring these locations is personally responsible for checking local conditions prior to departure. You are responsible for your own actions and decisions. The information contained in this work is based solely on the author's research at the time of publication and may not be accurate in the future. Neither the publisher nor the author assumes any liability for anyone climbing, exploring, visiting, or traveling to the locations described in this work. Climbing is dangerous by its nature. Any person engaging in mountain climbing is responsible for learning the proper techniques. The reader assumes all risks and accepts full responsibility for injuries, including death.

Sastrugi Press
PO Box 1297, Jackson, WY 83001, United States
www.sastrugipress.com
Quantity sales: Special discounts are available on quantity purchases by corporations, associations, and others. For details, contact the publisher at the address above.

Library of Congress Catalog-in-Publication Data
Library of Congress Control Number: 2017917786
Linsdau, Aaron
Arkansas Total Eclipse Guide / Aaron Linsdau-1st United States edition
p. cm.
1. Nature 2. Astronomy 3. Travel 4. Photography
Summary: Learn everything you need to know about viewing, experiencing, and photographing the total eclipse in Arkansas on April 8, 2024.

ISBN-13: 978-1-64922-324-1

508.4—dc23

All photography, maps and artwork by the author, except as noted.

10 9 8 7 6 5 4

Contents

Introduction

Thank you for purchasing this book. It has everything you need to know about the total eclipse in Arkansas on April 8, 2024.

A total eclipse passing through the United States is a rare event. The last US total eclipse was in 2017. It traveled from Oregon to South Carolina. The last American total eclipse prior to that was in 1979!

The next total eclipse over the US will not be until April 8, 2024. It will pass over Texas, Arkansas, the Midwest, and on to Maine. After that, the next coast-to-coast total eclipse will be in 2045.

It's imperative to make travel plans early. You will be amazed at the number of people swarming to the total eclipse path. Some might say watching a partial versus a total eclipse is a similar experience. It's not.

This book is written for Arkansas visitors and anyone else viewing the eclipse. You will find general planning, viewing, and photography information inside. Should you travel to the eclipse path in Arkansas in April, be prepared for an epic trip. The estimates based on the 2017 eclipse suggest that millions will converge on Arkansas.

Some hotels in the communities and cities along the path of totality in Arkansas have already been contacted by people to make reservations. Finding lodging along the eclipse path may be a major challenge.

Resources will be stretched far beyond the normal limits. Think gas lines from the late 1970s. It may be likely that traffic along highways will come to a complete standstill during this event. Be prepared with backup supplies.

Many smaller Arkansas towns are far from any major city. Arkansas country roads can be slow. Please obey posted speed limits for the safety of everyone. Be cautious about believing a map application's estimate of travel time in Arkansas.

People in communities along the path of the total eclipse may rent out properties for this event. With this major celestial spectacle in the spring of 2024, be assured that Arkansas "hasn't seen anything yet."

Is this to say to avoid Arkansas or other areas during the eclipse? Not at all! This guidebook provides ideas for interesting, alternative, and memorable locations to see the eclipse. It will be too late to rush to a better spot once the eclipse begins. Law enforcement will be out to help drivers reconsider speeding.

Please be patient and careful. There will be a large rush of people from all over the world, converging on Arkansas to enjoy the total eclipse. Be mindful of other drivers on eclipse weekend, as they may not be familiar with Arkansas roads.

You should feel compelled to play hooky on April 8. Ask for the day off. Take your kids out of school. They'll be adults before the next chance to see a total eclipse over America. Create family memories that will last a lifetime. Sastrugi Press does not normally advocate skipping school or work. Make an exception because this is too big an event to miss.

Wherever you plan to be along the total eclipse path, leave early and remember your eclipse glasses. People from all around the planet will converge on Arkansas. Be good to your fellow humans and be safe. We all want to enjoy this spectacular show.

Visit www.sastrugipress.com/eclipse for the latest updates for this state eclipse book series.

AUTHOR INFORMATION

Polar explorer and motivational speaker Aaron Linsdau's first book, *Antarctic Tears*, is an emotional journey into the heart of Antarctica. He ate two sticks of butter every day to survive. Aaron coughed up blood early in the expedition and struggled with equipment failures. Despite the endless difficulties, he set a world record for surviving the longest solo expedition to the South Pole.

Aaron teaches how to build resilience to overcome adversity by managing attitude. He shares his techniques for overcoming adrenaline burnout and constant overload. He inspires audiences to face their challenges with a new perspective. Aaron builds grit, teaches courage, and shows how to deal with uncontrollable change. He hopes that you will be inspired and have an enjoyable time watching the total eclipse in Arkansas.

Visit his website at www.aaronlinsdau.com or www.ncexped.com.

All About Arkansas

OVERVIEW OF ARKANSAS

For travelers who fancy exploration as a recreational activity, Arkansas has countless cultural and historical sites and attractions to experience. Whether you are traveling there before or after the eclipse, there is magnificent and nostalgic architecture, sites of social or literary interests, nature, and art galleries. The Natural State has plenty of these to keep you fully occupied. For example, its northwest Ozarks regions have magnificent limestone caves and hiking trails such as the Blanchard Spring Caverns. Little Rock, the state's capital, prides itself in hosting the William J. Clinton Presidential Center that houses the Bill Clinton presidential archives.

Arkansas is located in the south-central section of the United States and borders the Mississippi River. According to the state tourism board, Arkansas receives an estimated twenty-eight million visitors who spend over $7.2 billion in the state. Most of these tourists are drawn to Arkansas for its many recreational opportunities and outdoor sports, not to mention its natural beauty. This state boasts of its abundance in parks and vast wilderness areas that have terrain encompassing caves, hot springs, rivers, and mountains.

Whether one is in pursuit of a long getaway place or a simple Sunday afternoon drive, Arkansas affords visitors a wonderful opportunity to explore and appreciate its unique history, rich culture, and heritage. One of the advantages of Arkansas is tourist locations are distributed all across the state. History lovers and nature lovers enjoy boundless and nostalgic treats by strolling through quaint historic neighborhoods, visiting the eastern Arkansas Civil War battlefields, investigating caves in its northern reaches, or hiking in the Ouachita Mountains on the western border. They can also travel back in time while visiting glorious landmark sites like the Historic Arkansas Museum or the Old State House in Little Rock. For the adventurous, it's said that this site is even haunted.

Art admirers can treat themselves to the numerous excellent entertainment venues that the state has to offer, ranging from plays, poetry readings, and music. They can also celebrate the enriching African American cultural legacy experience provided at Mosaic Templars Cultural Center or visit the Delta Cultural Center to educate themselves on the King Biscuit Time radio show.

Hot Springs, a city in Arkansas's Ouachita Mountains, has a unique history. It has an anthology of splendid architecture and is an all-time favorite for many tourists. Back in the 1830s, settlers unveiled hot springs in this city that are said to contain medicinal powers. The city is said to have developed as a spa town that found favor in the eyes of celebrities and mobsters such as Lucky Luciano and Al Capone. These infamous criminals both came to enjoy the waters and gamble at Oaklawn Park Races.

The Craters of Diamonds is another must-visit site. The crater is a unique attraction site where tourists are allowed to dig for the precious stones and if they find something are allowed to keep their find. Covering 37.5 acres, this unique state park is described to have been the face of a volcanic mountain that exploded, raining diamonds on the Earth's surface about a million years ago. This is the place that Shirley Strawn is said to have discovered the Strawn Wagner Diamond. This particular stone is recognized as one of the world's only perfect diamonds.

While visiting Arkansas for the eclipse, you cannot fail to recognize that Arkansas is host to a people who never disappoint in making life a worthwhile experience. Almost every community in Arkansas supports celebrations or fairs of all sorts. From Conway's (Faulkner County) Toad Suck Daze, where they hold toad races, to Yellville's (Marion Country) turkey drops where they throw live turkeys from airplanes, Arkansas is always full of events.

Numerous tourist sites, attractions, and festivals define its image.

People who take their time to explore the state will always discover what makes Arkansas special. Whether you prefer listening to blues on the Mississippi banks, exploring nature walks among wildflowers, or treating yourself to tasty meals at mom-and-pop restaurants, Arkansas is a place where you can experience it all.

Hotels and Motels During the Eclipse

Once excitement of the total eclipse over Arkansas spreads, rooms will become scarce. Many hotels in towns along the path of totality in western states sold out for a year or more during the 2017 total eclipse. Arkansas is not alone in this challenge. Hotels all along the path of totality will sell out in anticipation of the 2024 total eclipse.

What does this mean for eclipse visitors? Lodging and room rentals in eclipse towns will be at a massive premium. Does that mean all hope is lost to find a place to stay? Not at all. But you will have to be creative. There will be few, if any, hotel rooms available in these eclipse cities by early 2024. Accommodations in the cities and towns along the path of the eclipse will be difficult to come by.

In summer 2017, the author searched on Hotels.com for rooms along the 2017 total eclipse path on the weekend of August 21 and found many major cities sold out. Once word of the 2024 eclipse spreads, room rates will increase and availability will drop.

Search for rooms farther away from the eclipse path. If you are willing to stay in cities outside the eclipse path, you will have better success at finding rooms. As the eclipse approaches, people will book rooms farther from the totality path. By early spring, rooms in cities near the total eclipse path may be unavailable. The effect of this event will be felt across Arkansas and the rest of the United States.

Think regionally when looking for rooms. Be prepared to search far and wide during this major event. If a five-hour drive is manageable, your lodging options greatly expand, but it also increases your travel risk.

Internet Rentals

To find rooms to stay in towns along the eclipse path, try a web service such as Airbnb.com. Note that some people rent out rooms or homes illegally, against zoning regulations. Cities will feel the crunch of inquiries early due to others who experienced the 2017 eclipse.

If cities fully enforce zoning laws, authorities may prevent your weekend home rental. Online home rentals during the eclipse will be a target for rental scams. People from out of the area steal photos and descriptions, then post the home for rent. You send your check or wire money to a "rental agent" then show up to find you have been scammed. If the deal sounds strange or too good to be true, run away.

Camping

If you can book a campsite, do it as soon as you can. Do not wait. All areas in the national forests are first-come, first-served. Forest roads may be packed. Expect all areas to be swarming with people. Show up early to stake out your spot. Consider staying farther away and driving early on April 8.

Please respect private land too. Arkansas folks don't take kindly to people overrunning their property without permission. In a big state with millions of residents, people are very protective, but they're friendly, too. You never know what you might be able to arrange with a smile and a bit of money.

This all said, there are plenty of camping opportunities throughout Arkansas. You don't have to sleep exactly on the eclipse path. If you're ready to rough it, there are national forest camping options.

Government agencies will meet years in advance to talk about how to manage the influx of people. Every possible government agency will be working full time to enforce the various rules and regulations.

National Parks and Monuments

Finding a camping site at any state park, national park, or national monument along the eclipse path in Arkansas will be challenging. To watch the eclipse from any location, you do not have to sleep in it. You just need to drive there in the morning.

Law enforcement will be present on the eclipse weekend. Hundreds of thousands of people are expected in the region. Parking may overflow. It will make parking lots and lines on Black Friday at the mall look uncrowded. For an event of this magnitude, find your location as early as possible.

The first sentence of the national parks mission statement is:
"The National Park Service preserves unimpaired the natural and cultural resources and values of the national park system for the enjoyment, education, and inspiration of this and future generations."

Roadside camping (sleeping in your car) is not allowed in national monuments or parks. Park facilities are only designed to handle so many people per day. Water, trash collection, and toilets can only withstand so much. If you notice trash on the ground, take a moment to throw it away. Protect your national park and help out. Rangers are diligent and hardworking but they can only do so much to manage the expected crowds.

National Forests and Wilderness

There are national forest options in Arkansas. They all have camping opportunities. The forest service manages undeveloped and primitive campsites. Be sure to check for any fire restrictions. Check with individual agencies for last-minute information and regulations. The forest service requires proper food storage. Plan to purchase food and water before choosing your campsite. Below is a partial list of national forests along or near the total eclipse path:

Ouachita NF:
https://www.fs.usda.gov/ouachita
Ozark NF:
https://www.fs.usda.gov/osfnf

Backcountry service roads abound in Arkansas. Maps for forests are available at local visitor centers and bookstores. This book's website has digital copies of some forest maps.

Printed national forest maps are large and detailed. They have illustrated road paths, connections, and other vital travel information not available on digital device maps. Viewing digital maps on your smartphone or mobile pad is difficult. If you plan to camp in the forest, a real paper map is a wise investment.

Camping in federal wilderness areas is also allowed. Those areas afford the ultimate backcountry experience. However, be aware that no vehicle travel is allowed in the specially designated areas. This ban includes: vehicles, bikes, hang gliders, and drones. You can travel only on foot or with pack animals.

SLEEP IN YOUR CAR

Countless RVs, campers, trucks, cars, and motorcycles will flood Arkansas. Sleeping in your car with friends is tolerable. Doing so with unadventurous spouses or children is another matter.

Do not be caught along the path of the total eclipse without some sort of plan, especially in the bigger cities of Arkansas. The whole path of totality will fill with people on April 8.

USEFUL LOCAL WEBCAMS

Local webcams are handy to make last-minute travel decisions. Modern webcams are sensitive enough to show headlights at night. Use them to determine if there are issues before traveling out. Eclipse traffic will add to the morning commuter traffic.

There are smartphone applications which are useful to check webcams in many locations. Consult your device's app store for the latest updates. Whether you use an app or computer, an Internet search will reveal many handy webcams for your eclipse planning.

Weather

It's all about the weather during the eclipse. Nothing else will matter if the sky is cloudy. You can be nearly anywhere along the path in Arkansas and catch a view of the event when traffic comes to a standstill. But if there's a cloud cover forecast, seriously reconsider your viewing location.

Travel early wherever you plan to go. Attempting to change locations an hour before the eclipse due to weather will likely cause you to miss the event. Arkansas country roads can be narrow and slow. The number of vehicles will cause unexpected backups.

MODERN FORECASTS

Use a smartphone application to check the up-to-date weather. Wunderground is a good application and has relatively reliable forecasts for the region. The hourly forecast for the same day has been rather accurate for the last two years. The below discussion refers to features found in the Wunderground app. However, any application with detailed weather views will improve your eclipse forecasting skills.

CLOUD COVER FORECAST

The most useful forecast view is the visible and infrared cloud-coverage map. Avoid downloading this app the night before and trying to learn how to read it. Practice reading them at home. It's imperative to understand how to interpret the maps early.

Infrared cloud map showing the worst case eclipse cloud cover. Courtesy of National Weather Service.

All cloud cover, night or day, will appear on an infrared map. Warm, low-altitude clouds are shown in white and gray. High-altitude cold clouds are displayed in shades of green, yellow, red, and purple. Anything other than a clear map spells eclipse-viewing problems.

To improve your weather guess, use the animated viewer of the cloud cover. It will give you a sense of cloud motion. You can discern whether clouds or rain are moving toward, away from, or circulating around your location.

NORMAL ARKANSAS WEATHER PATTERN

Due to the direction of the jet stream, most weather travels across the Pacific Ocean, through the western states, over the Rockies, and then into Arkansas. On occasion, weather can approach from Mexico or off the Gulf of Mexico. Due to the nature of the tropical storms from the Atlantic, weather in Arkansas can be unpredictable.

The common weather pattern in April is slightly warm in the afternoon and mildly cool in the evenings. Passing cold fronts in spring can bring unexpected cloud cover and rains.

Historically, Arkansas tends to have moderate cloud cover during April. Prepare to make adjustments. If anything other than clear skies are predicted, drive to other parts of Texas, Arkansas, or Oklahoma.

Be aware of tornadoes in Arkansas. Although the peak tornado season is June, there have been many recorded tornadoes in April. Pay attention to the weather forecast. If dangerous weather is predicted, your main concern should be safety rather than chasing an eclipse.

Consider that slow-moving clouds can obscure the sun for far longer than the four-minute duration of the totality. The time of totality is so short that you do not want to risk it. Missing it due to a single cloud will be a major disappointment.

Local Eclipse Weather Forecasts

Local town and city newspapers, radio, and television stations around Arkansas will have a weekend edition with articles discussing the eclipse weather. However, conditions change unpredictably in Arkansas. A three-day forecast may be incorrect.

Forest Fires

For the past several years, forest fires have been common in the United States. The spring of 2024 will likely to be no different. There have been fires in the Arkansas during spring. With the ongoing drought, there will possibly be fires again during the time of the eclipse. For fire updates check:

inciweb.nwcg.gov

For the best eclipse viewing experience, you need to have as clear a sky as possible. Fog, clouds, or smoke will obscure the subtleties of the sun's corona. If you think the view of the sky is going to be blocked, don't wait until the last minute to move to a clearer location. If you wait too long to decide to move to a better viewing area, it may be impossible due to traffic.

Road Closures Due to Fires

Highways connecting various Arkansas towns can be closed during wildfires. During March, 2013, there were five large fire incidents including the Iron Mountain, White 1, and Fire Truck Fires.

With unpredictable weather in the last few years, it's a guess what will happen in April 2024. If forest areas continue to remain dry, the whole region may have fires.

Although fire is an important part of forest ecology, it worries eclipse chasers. Other than clouds, smoke from fires will block the view of the sun and moon on the morning of the eclipse. Should there be fires where you are or may be headed, reconsider your location as early as possible. The most accurate website for fires is:

inciweb.nwcg.gov

Check the Arkansas road report for updated information:

www.idrivearkansas.com

It's imperative to plan for fires and their effects. Watch the weather reports. If strong winds and lightning storms are forecast, prepare to change your viewing location. If conditions are poor, you and thousands of other vehicles will be trapped in slow-moving traffic.

If you believe it's necessary to leave a town to watch the eclipse, do so the night before or extremely early in the morning. RVs are common, and trains of them crawl through popular areas.

Arkansas Information

Cellular Phones

Cellular "cell" phone service in remote Arkansas locations may be problematic. Most of the time there is good coverage along the main highways and interstates. However, even along major thoroughfares, there can be little or no coverage.

It's possible to find zones where text messages will send when phone calls are impossible. If you cannot make a phone call, the chance of having data coverage for web surfing or e-mail is low.

Please look up any information or communicate what you need before departing from the main roads around Arkansas. Bureau of Land Management (BLM) areas sometimes have coverage. Planned to be self-contained. Plan for your cell phone not to connect.

You may find yourself out of cell service. With a large number of cell users in a concentrated area, coverage and data speed may collapse as well. Search on the phrase "cell phone coverage breathing".

ARKANSAS

Wilderness and Forest Safety

All Arkansas mountains and wilderness areas are full of wild animals. Although beautiful, wild animals can be dangerous. They can easily injure or kill people, as they are far more powerful than humans. Do not try to feed any wild animals, including squirrels, foxes, and chipmunks, as they can carry diseases. These suggestions apply to all public lands.

FERAL HOGS

Introduced in the early twentieth century, hogs have become a major problem in Arkansas. Although they tend to flee when encountered, hogs have been known to attack people. They can be aggressive and their tusks can inflict serious wounds. There have been instances of deaths, too. It is best to leave these animals alone if you encounter one.

ALLIGATORS

Although the chance of encountering an alligator is low, it is not uncommon to encounter them. With hurricanes moving significant quantities of water in recent years, alligators may be in unexpected locations. If you encounter one, back away from the animal and contact fish and game if it poses a threat.

VENOMOUS SNAKES

There are multiple species of venomous snakes in Arkansas including the Western Diamondback & Timber Rattlesnakes, Pygmy, Copper-

ARKANSAS

head, Coral Snake, and Cottonmouth. Although these reptiles are not generally aggressive, they can strike when provoked or threatened. Of the approximately 8,000 people annually bitten by venomous snakes in the United States, ten to fifteen people die according to the U.S. Food and Drug Administration.

The best way to avoid rattlesnake encounters is to be mindful of your environment. Do not place your hands or feet in locations where you cannot clearly see the surroundings. Avoid heavy brush or tall weeds where snakes hide during the day. Step on a log or rock rather than over it, as a hidden snake might be on the other side. Rattlesnakes may not make any noise before striking.

Avoid handling all snakes. Should you be bitten, stay calm and call 911 or emergency dispatch as soon as possible. Transport the victim to the nearest medical facility immediately. Rapid professional treatment is the best way to manage rattlesnake bites. Refer to US Forest Service and professional medical texts for more information on managing rattlesnakes injuries.

BEARS

The forests of Arkansas are home to black bears. Safety is imperative around these powerful animals. Although they often appear docile, they can become aggressive if threatened. In the unlikely event of an attack, fight back against the bear. Use whatever you have at your disposal to defend yourself. Report all negative or aggressive bears to the local authorities.

If a bear hears you, it will usually vacate the area. Bear charges are often caused by unexpected and surprise encounters. Noise is the best defense to avoid surprising bears. Regularly clap, make noise, and talk loudly. The University of Arkansas Division of Agriculture website has more specific information on safety and food management in bear country at www.uaex.edu/publications/pdf/FSA-9087.pdf.

It is recommended to stay one hundred yards (300 feet) away from all bears. They are exciting to see but need their space. Refer to current forest or park regulations for more safety information.

ARKANSAS

Mountain Lions

Though listed as extinct in the state, there have been recent reports of mountain lions in Arkansas by the Arkansas Game and Fish Commission. If you encounter a mountain lion, do not run. Keep calm, back away slowly, and maintain eye contact. Do all you can to appear larger. Stand upright, raise your arms, or hoist your jacket. Never bend over or crouch down. If attacked, fight back.

Eclipse Day Safety

1. Hydrate

Spring temperatures are usually mild to warm. The excitement of the event can distract you from managing hydration. Drink plenty of water. Consume more than you would at home.

2. Eye Safety time

Use certified eclipse safety glasses at all times when viewing the partial eclipse. Only remove the glasses when the totality happens. Give your eyes time to rest. They can dry out and become irritated. Bring FDA approved eye drops to keep your eyes moist.

3. Sun exposure

Facing at the sun for three hours can result in sunburns. Wear sunglasses and liberally apply sunscreen to avoid sunburns.

4. Eat well

Keep your energy up. Appetite loss is common when traveling. Maintain your normal eating schedule.

5. Prepare for temperature changes

Temperatures will drop rapidly during the eclipse and also once the sun sets. Bring appropriate clothing.

6. Talk with your doctor

If the humidity or heat bothers you talk with your doctor before traveling. Seek professional medical attention for serious symptoms.

ARKANSAS

Total eclipse path across the United States (approximate).

Total eclipse path across Arkansas (approximate).

All About Eclipses

How an Eclipse Happens

An eclipse occurs when one celestial body falls in line with another, thus obscuring the sun from view. This occurs much more often than you'd think, considering how many bodies there are in the solar system. For instance, there are over 150 moons in the solar system. On Earth, we have two primary celestial bodies: the sun and the moon. The entire solar system is constantly in motion, with planets orbiting the sun and moons orbiting the planets. These celestial bodies often come into alignment. When these alignments cause the sun to be blocked, it is called an eclipse.

For an eclipse to occur, the sun, Earth, and moon must be in alignment. There are two types of eclipses: solar and lunar. A solar eclipse occurs when the moon obscures the sun. A lunar eclipse occurs when the moon passes through Earth's shadow. Solar eclipses are much more common, as we experience an average of 240 solar eclipses a century compared to an average of 150 lunar eclipses. Despite this, we are more likely to see a lunar eclipse than a solar eclipse. This is due to the visibility of each.

For a solar eclipse to be visible, you have to be in the moon's shadow. The problem with viewing a total eclipse is that the moon casts a small shadow over the world at any given time. You have to be in

ECLIPSES

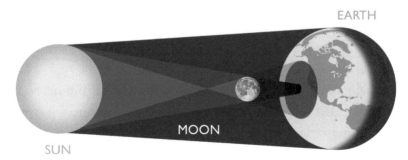

EARTH

MOON

SUN

* ILLUSTRATION NOT TO SCALE

a precise location to view a total eclipse. The issue that arises is that most of these locations are inaccessible to most people. Though many would like to see a total solar eclipse, most aren't about to set sail for the middle of the Pacific Ocean. In fact, a solar eclipse is visible in the same place on the world on average every 375 years. This means that if you miss a solar eclipse above your hometown, you're not going to see another one unless you travel or move.

It's much easier to catch a glimpse of a lunar eclipse, even though they occur at a much lower frequency than their solar counterparts. A lunar eclipse darkens the moon for a few hours. This is different than a new moon when it faces away from the sun. During these eclipses, the moon fades and becomes nearly invisible.

Another result of a lunar eclipse is a blood moon. Earth's atmosphere bends a small amount of sunlight onto the moon turning it orange-red. The blood moon is caused by the dawn or dusk light being refracted onto the moon during an eclipse.

Lunar eclipses are much easier to see. Even when the moon is in the shadow of Earth, it's still visible throughout the world because of how much smaller it is than Earth.

Total vs. Partial Eclipse

What is the difference between a partial and total eclipse? A total eclipse of either the sun or the moon will occur only when the sun, Earth, and the moon are aligned in a perfectly straight line. This ensures that either the sun or the moon is partially or completely obscured.

In contrast, a partial eclipse occurs when the alignment of the three celestial bodies is not in a perfectly straight line. These types of eclipses usually result in only a part of either the sun or the moon being obscured. This is often what led to ancient civilizations believing that some form of magical beast or deity was eating the sun or the moon. It appears as though something has taken a bite out of either the sun or the moon during a partial eclipse.

Total eclipses, rarer than partial eclipses, still occur quite often. It's more difficult for people to be in a position to experience such an event firsthand. Total solar eclipses can only be viewed from a small portion of the world that falls into the darkest part of the moon's shadow. Often this happens in the middle of the ocean.

THE MOON'S SHADOW

The moon's shadow is divided into two parts: the umbra and the penumbra. The former is much smaller than the latter, as the umbra is the innermost and darkest part of the shadow. The umbra is thus the central point of the moon's shadow, meaning that it is extremely small in comparison to the entire shadow. For a total solar eclipse to be visible, you need to be directly beneath the umbra of the moon's shadow. This is because that is the only point at which the moon completely blocks the view of the sun.

In contrast, the penumbra is the region of the moon's shadow in which only a portion of the light cast by the sun is obscured. When

Total eclipse shadow 2016 as seen from 1 million miles on the Deep Space Climate Observatory satellite. Courtesy of NASA.

standing in the penumbra, you are viewing the eclipse at an angle. In the penumbra, the moon does not completely block the sun from view. This means that while the event is a total solar eclipse, you'll only see a partial eclipse. The umbra for the April 8 eclipse is over one hundred miles wide. The penumbra will cover much of the United States.

To provide some context, one total solar eclipse we experienced occurred on March 9, 2016, and was visible as a partial eclipse across most of the Pacific Ocean, parts of Asia, and Australia. However, the only place in the world to view this total solar eclipse was in a few parts of Indonesia.

Due to the varied locations and the brief periods for which they're visible, it's difficult to see each and every eclipse that occurs. The umbra of the moon is such a small fraction of the entire shadow and the majority of our planet is comprised of water. Thus, the rarity of being able to view a total solar eclipse increases significantly because it's likely that the umbra will fall over some part of the ocean rather than a populated landmass. There are not total or annular eclipses every month because the moon's orbit is 5.1° off the ecliptic plane of the Earth and sun.

Eclipses Throughout History

Ancient peoples believed eclipses were from the wrath of angry gods, portents of doom and misfortune, or wars between celestial beings. Eclipses have played many roles in cultures, creating myths since the dawn of time. Both solar and lunar eclipses affected societies worldwide. Inspiring fear, curiosity, and the creation of legends, eclipses have cast a long shadow in the collective unconscious of humanity throughout history.

Early Myth & Astronomy

Documented observations of solar eclipses have been found as far back in history as ancient Egyptian and Chinese records. Timekeeping was important to ancient Chinese cultures. Astronomical observations were an integral factor in the Chinese calendar. The first observation of a solar eclipse is found in Chinese records from over 4,000 years ago. Evidence suggests that ancient Egyptian observations may predate those archaic writings.

Many ancient societies, including Roman, Greek and Chinese civilizations, were able to infer and foresee solar eclipses from astronomical data. The sudden and unpredictable nature of solar eclipses had a stressful and intimidating effect on many societies that lacked the scientific insight to accurately predict astronomical events. Relying on the sun for their agricultural livelihood, those societies interpreted solar eclipses as world-threatening disasters.

In ancient Vietnam, solar eclipses were explained as a giant frog eating the sun. The peasantry of ancient Greece believed that an eclipse was the sign of a furious godhead, presenting an omen of wrathful retribution in the form of natural disasters. Other cultures were less speculative in their investigations. The Chinese Song Dynasty scientist Shen Kuo proved the spherical nature of the Earth and heavenly bodies through scientific insight gained by the study of eclipses.

ECLIPSES

The Eclipse in Native American Mythology

Eclipses have played a significant role in the history of the United States. Before Europeans settled in the Americas, solar eclipses were important astronomical events to Native American cultures. In most native cultures, an eclipse was a particularly bad omen. Both the sun and the moon were regarded as sacred. Viewing an eclipse, or even being outside for the duration of the event, was considered highly taboo by the Navajo culture. During an eclipse, men and women would simply avert their eyes from the sky, acting as though it was not happening.

The Choctaw people had a unique story to explain solar eclipses. Considering the event as the mischievous actions of a black squirrel and its attempt to eat the sun, the Choctaw people would do their best to scare away the cosmic squirrel by making as much noise as possible until the end of the event, at which point cognitive bias would cause them to believe they'd once again averted disaster on an interplanetary scale.

CONTEMPORARY AMERICAN SOLAR PHENOMENA

The investigation of solar phenomena in twentieth-century American history had a similarly profound effect on the people of the United States. A total solar eclipse occurring on the sixteenth of June, 1806, engulfed the entire country. It started near modern-day Arizona. It passed across the Midwest, over Ohio, Pennsylvania, New York, Massachusetts, and Connecticut. The 1806 total eclipse was notable for being one of the first publicly advertised solar events. The public was informed beforehand of the astronomical curiosity through a pamphlet written by Andrew Newell entitled *Darkness at Noon, or the Great Solar Eclipse.*

This pamphlet described local circumstances and went into great detail explaining the true nature of the phenomenon, dispelling myth and superstition, and even giving questionable advice on the best methods of viewing the sun during the event. Replete with a short historical record of eclipses through the ages, the *Darkness at Noon* pamphlet is one of the first examples of an attempt to capitalize on the mysterious nature of solar eclipses.

Another notable American solar eclipse occurred on June 8, 1918. Passing over the United States from Washington to Florida, the eclipse was accurately predicted by the U.S. Naval Observatory and heavily documented in the newspapers of the day. Howard Russell Butler, painter and founder of the American Fine Arts Society, painted the eclipse from the U.S. Naval Observatory, immortalizing the event in *The Oregon Eclipse.*

Four more total solar eclipses occurred over the United States in the years 1923, 1925, 1932, and 1954, with another occurring in 1959. The October 2, 1959, solar eclipse began over Boston, Massachusetts. It was a sunrise event that was unviewable from the ground level. Eminent astronomer Jay Pasachoff attributed this event to sparking his interest in the study of astronomy. Studying under Professor Donald Menzel of Williams College, Pasachoff was able to view the event from an airline hired by his professor.

To this day, many myths surround the eclipse. In India, some local customs require fasting. In eastern Africa, eclipses are seen as a danger to pregnant women and young children. Despite the mystery and legend associated with unique and rare astronomical events, eclipses continue to be awe-inspiring. Even in the modern day, eclipses draw out reverential respect for the inexorable passing of celestial bodies. They are a reminder of the intimate relationship between the denizens of Earth and the universe at large.

Present Day Eclipses

The year 2017 brought the world's most-watched total eclipse in history on August 21, when a total solar eclipse crossed the United States. An annular eclipse, a "ring of fire," will pass over the United States in 2023 from Oregon to Texas. Though impressive, it will not

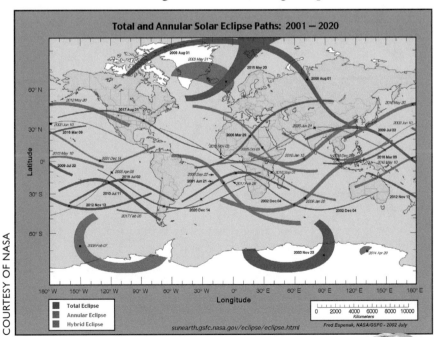

ECLIPSES

COURTESY OF NASA

compare to the 2024 total eclipse. There is little in nature that equals the spectacle of the sun's corona and seeing stars in the day.

There will be multiple partial, annular, or hybrid eclipses across the world before the 2024 total eclipse. However many are in remote, inaccessible, or potentially dangerous locations on the globe. In 2019 and 2020, Chile and Argentina will experience total eclipses. The next total eclipse after that will occur over Antarctica in 2021. An extremely rare hybrid eclipse will happen in 2023 over the Indian Ocean, Australia, and Indonesia.

The next total solar eclipse viewable from the United States will occur on April 8, 2024. It will be visible in fourteen states: Texas, Oklahoma, Arkansas, Missouri, Kentucky, Illinois, Indiana, Ohio, Pennsylvania, Michigan, New York, Vermont, New Hampshire, and Maine.

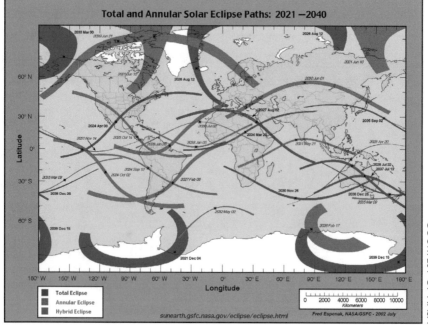

COURTESY OF NASA

Viewing and Photographing the Eclipse

AT-HOME PINHOLE METHOD

Use the pinhole method to view the eclipse safely. It costs little but is the safest technique there is. Take a stiff piece of single-layer cardboard and punch a clean pinhole. Let the sun shine through the pinhole onto another piece of cardboard. That's it!

Never look at the sun through the pinhole. Your back should be toward the sun to protect your eyes. To brighten the image, simply move the back piece of cardboard closer to the pinhole. To see it larger, move the back cardboard farther away. Do not make the pinhole larger. It will only distort the crescent sun.

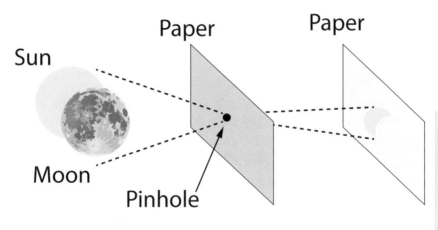

PHOTOGRAPHY

WELDING GOGGLES

Welding goggles that have a rating of fourteen or higher are another useful eclipse viewing tool. The goggles can be used to view the solar eclipse directly. Do not use the goggles to look through binoculars or telescopes, as the goggles could potentially shatter due to intense direct heat. Avoid long periods of gazing with the goggles. Look away every so often. Give your eyes a break.

SOLAR FILTERS FOR TELESCOPES

The ONLY safe way to view solar eclipses using telescopes or binoculars is to use solar filters. The filters are coated with metal to diminish the full intensity of the sun. Although the filters can be expensive, it is better to purchase a quality filter rather than an inexpensive one that could shatter or melt from the heat.

The filters attach to the front of the telescope for easy viewing. Remember to give your telescope cooling breaks. Rapid heating can damage your equipment with or without filters attached.

Watch Out for Unsafe Filters

There are several myths surrounding solar filters for eclipse viewing. In order for filters to be safe, they must be specially designed for looking at a solar eclipse. The following are all unsafe for eclipse viewing and can lead to retinal damage: developed colored or chromogenic film, black-and-white negatives such as X-rays, CDs with aluminum, smoked glass, floppy disk covers, black-and-white film with no silver, sunglasses, or polarizing films.

Watch Out for Unsafe Eclipse Glasses

During the 2017 total eclipse, several vendors sold eclipse glasses that were not safe for viewing the sun. Although they were marketed as safe and were even marked with the ISO 12312-2 certification, they did not block eye-damaging visible, infrared, and ultraviolet light. Check the American Astronomical Society's website (eclipse.aas.org) for a list of reputable eclipse glasses vendors.

Viewing with Binoculars

When viewing the eclipse with binoculars, it is important to use solar filters on both lenses until totality. Only then is it safe to remove the filter. As the sun becomes visible after totality, replace the filters for safe viewing. Protect your pupils. Remember to give your binoculars a cool-down break between viewings. They can overheat rapidly from being pointed directly at the sun even with filters attached.

Planning Ahead

There are many things to keep in mind when viewing a total eclipse. It is important to plan ahead to get the most out of this extraordinary experience.

PHOTOGRAPHY

UNDERSTANDING SUN POSITION

All compass bearings in this book are true north. All compasses point to Earth's magnetic north. The difference between these two measurements is called magnetic declination. The magnetic declination for Arkansas is:

0° 14' E ± 0° 21' (for Little Rock in 2020)

Adjust the declination from the azimuth bearing as given in the text, and set your compass to that direction.

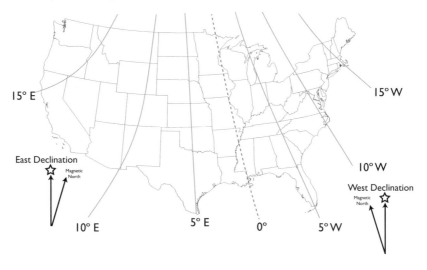

If you purchase a compass with a built-in declination adjustment, you can change the setting once and eliminate the calculations. The Suunto M-3G compass has this correction. A compass with a sighting mirror or wire will help you make a more accurate azimuth sighting.

The Suunto M-3G also has an inclinometer. This allows you to measure the elevation of any object above the horizon. Use this to figure out how high the sun will be above your position.

You can also use a smartphone inclinometer and compass for this purpose. Make sure to calibrate your smartphone's compass before every use, otherwise it might indicate the wrong bearing. Set the smartphone compass for true north to match the book. Understand the compass prior to April 8. There will be little time to guess or search on Google. Smartphone and GPS compasses are "sticky." Their compasses don't swing as freely as a magnetic compass does.

The author has used his magnetic compass for azimuth measurements and a smartphone to measure elevation. Combining these two tools will allow you to make the best sightings possible.

Outdoor sporting goods stores in most towns and cities carry compasses. Purchase and practice with a good compass in your hometown well before the event. Take the time to learn how to use it before the day of the eclipse. You do not want to struggle with orienteering basics under pressure.

Sun Azimuth

Azimuth is the compass angle along the horizon, with 0° corresponding to north, and increasing in a clockwise direction. 90° is east, 180° is south, and 270° is west.

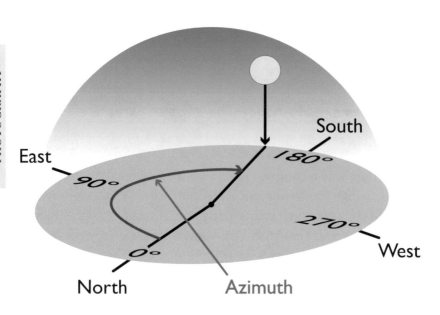

PHOTOGRAPHY

Sun Elevation

Altitude is the sun's angle up from the horizon. A 0° altitude means exactly on the horizon and 90° means "straight up."

Using the sun azimuth and elevation data, you can predict the position of the sun at any given time. Positions given in this book coincide with the time of eclipse totality unless otherwise noted.

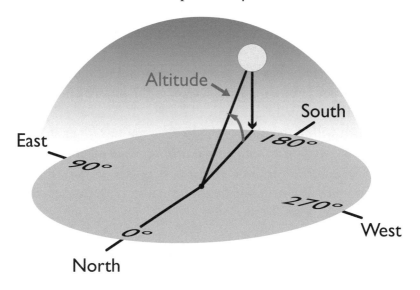

ECLIPSE DATA FOR SELECT ARKANSAS LOCATIONS

LOCATION	TOTALITY START (CDT)	ALTITUDE	AZIMUTH
HOT SPRINGS NP	1:49:20PM	61°	198°
JONESBORO	1:55:28PM	59°	205°
LITTLE ROCK	1:51:29PM	61°	201°
MARSHALL	1:51:49PM	60°	200°
PARAGOULD	1:55:52PM	59°	205°
TEXARKANA	1:46:48PM	63°	196°

PHOTOGRAPHY

ECLIPSE PHOTOGRAPHY

Photographing an eclipse is an exciting challenge, as the moon's shadow moves near 1,600MPH. There is an element of danger and the pressure of time. Looking at the unfiltered sun through a camera can permanently damage your vision and your camera. If you are unsure, just enjoy the eclipse with specially designed eclipse glasses. Keep a solar filter on your lens during the eclipse and remove for the duration of totality!

PARTIAL VS. TOTAL SOLAR ECLIPSE

To successfully and safely photograph a partial and total eclipse, it is important to understand the difference between the two. A solar eclipse occurs when the moon is positioned between the sun and Earth. The region where the shadow of the moon falls upon Earth's surface is where a solar eclipse is visible.

The moon's shadow has two parts—the penumbral shadow and the umbral shadow. The penumbral shadow is the moon's outer shadow where partial solar eclipses can be observed. Total solar eclipses can only be seen within the umbral shadow, the moon's inner shadow.

You cannot say you've seen a total eclipse when all you saw was a partial solar eclipse. It is like saying you've watched a concert, but in reality, you only listened outside the arena. In both cases, you have missed the drama and the action.

PHOTOGRAPHING A PARTIAL AND TOTAL SOLAR ECLIPSE

Aside from the region where the outer shadow of the moon is cast, a partial solar eclipse is also visible before a total solar eclipse within

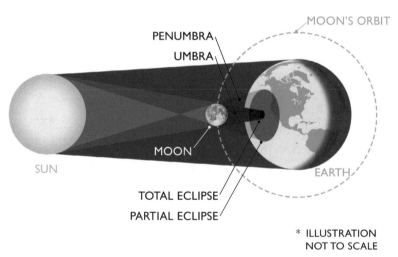

the inner shadow region. In both cases, it is imperative to use a solar filter on the lens for both photography and safety reasons. This is the only difference between taking a partial eclipse and a total eclipse photograph of the sun.

To photograph a total solar eclipse, you must be within the Path of Totality, the surface of the Earth within the moon's umbral shadow.

THE CHALLENGE

A total solar eclipse only lasts for a couple of minutes. It is brief, but the scenario it brings is unforgettable. Seeing the radiant sun slowly being covered by darkness gives the spectator a high level of anticipation and indescribable excitement. Once the moon completely covers the sun's radiance, the corona is finally visible. In the darkness, the sun's corona shines, capturing the crowd's full attention. Watching this phenomenon is a breathtaking experience.

Amidst all the noise, cheering, and excitement, you have no more than a few minutes to take a perfect photograph. The key to this is planning. You need to plan, practice, and perfect what you will do when the big moment arrives because there is no replay. The pressure is enormous. You only have a short time to capture the totality and the sun's corona using different exposures.

PLAN, PRACTICE, PERFECT

It is important to practice photographing before the actual phenomenon arrives. Test your chosen imaging setup for flaws. Rehearse over and over until your body remembers what you will do from the moment you arrive at your chosen spot to the moment you pack up and leave the area.

You will discover potential problems regarding vibrations and focus that you can address immediately. This minimizes the variables that might affect your photographs at the most critical moment.

It's common for experienced eclipse chasers to lose track of what they plan to do. Write down what you expect to do. Practice it time and again. Play annoying, distracting music while you practice. Try photographing in the worst weather possible. Do anything you can to practice under pressure. Eclipse day is not the time to practice.

Once the sun is completely covered, don't just take photographs. Capture the experience and the image of the total solar eclipse in your mind as well. Set up cameras around you to record not just the total solar eclipse but also the excitement and reaction of the crowd.

PHOTOGRAPHY

ECLIPSE PHOTOGRAPHY GEAR

What do you need to photograph the total eclipse? There are only a few pieces of equipment that you'll need. Preparing to photograph an eclipse successfully takes time. Not only do you have to be skilled and have the right gear, you have to be in the correct place.

BASIC ECLIPSE PHOTOGRAPHY EQUIPMENT

- Solar viewing glasses (verify authenticity)
- Lens solar filter
- Minimum 300mm lens
- Stable tripod that can be tilted to 60° vertical
- High-resolution DSLR
- Spare batteries for everything
- Secondary camera to photograph people, the horizon, etc.
- Remote cable or wireless release

ADDITIONAL ITEMS

- Video camera
- Video camera tripod
- Quality pair of binoculars
- Solar filters for each binocular lens
- Photo editing software

EQUIPMENT TO PREPARE BEFORE THE BIG DAY

A. Solar viewing glasses

You need a pair of solar viewing glasses as the eclipse approaches.

B. Solar Filter

Partial and total eclipse photography is different from normal photography. Even if only 1% of the sun's surface is visible, it is still approximately 10,000 times brighter than the moon. Before totality, use a solar filter on your lens. Do not look at the sun with your eyes. It can cause irreparable damage to your retinas.

DO NOT leave your camera pointed at the sun without a solar filter attached. The sun will melt the inside of your camera. Think of a magnifying glass used to torch ants and multiply that by one hundred.

PHOTOGRAPHY

C. Lens

To capture the corona's majesty, you need to use a telescope or a telephoto lens. The best focal length, which will give you a large image of the sun's disk, is 400mm and above. You don't want to waste all your efforts by bringing home a small dot where the black disk and majestic corona are supposed to be.

D. Tripod

Bring a stable enough tripod to support your camera properly to avoid unsteady shots and repeated adjustments. Either will ruin your photos. It also needs to be portable in case you need to change locations for a better shot. *Shut off camera stabilization on a tripod!*

E. Camera

You need to remember to set your camera to its highest resolution to capture all the details. Set your camera to:

- 14-bit RAW is ideal, otherwise
- JPG, Fine compression, Maximum resolution

Bracket your exposures. Shoot at various shutter speeds to capture different brightnesses in the corona. Note that stopping your lens all the way down may not result in the sharpest images.

Choose the lowest possible ISO for the best quality while maintaining a high shutter speed to prevent blurred shots. Set your camera to manual. Do not use AUTO ISO. Your camera will be fooled. The night before, test the focus position of your lens using a bright star or the moon.

Constantly double-check your focus. Be paranoid about this. You can deal with a grainy picture. No amount of Photoshop will fix a blurry, out-of-focus picture.

F. Batteries

Remember to bring fresh batteries! Make sure that you have enough power to capture the most important moments. Swap in fresh batteries thirty minutes before totality.

PHOTOGRAPHY

G. Remote release

Use a wired or wireless remote release to fire the camera's shutter. This will reduce the amount of camera vibration.

H. Video Camera

Run a video camera of yourself. Capture all the things you say and do during the totality. You'll be amazed at your reaction.

I. Photo editing software

You will need quality photo editing software to process your eclipse images. Adobe Lightroom and Photoshop are excellent programs to extract the most out of your images. Become well versed in how to use them at least a month before the eclipse.

J. Smartphone applications

The following smartphone applications will aid in your photography planning: Wunderground, Skyview, Photographer's Ephemeris, Sunrise and Sunset Calculator, SunCalc, and Sun Surveyor among others.

CAMERA PHONES

Smartphone cameras are useful for many things but not eclipse photography. An iPhone 6 camera has a 63° horizontal field of view and is 3264 pixels across. If you attempt to photograph the eclipse, the sun will be a measly 30-40 pixels wide depending on the phone. Digital pinch zoom won't help here. If you want *National Geographic* images, you'll need a serious camera and lens, far beyond any smartphone.

Consider instead using a smartphone to run a time-lapse of the entire event. The sun will be minuscule when shot on a smartphone. Think of something else exciting and interesting do to with it. Purchase a Gorilla Pod, inexpensive tripod, or selfie stick and mount the smartphone somewhere unique.

Also, partial and total eclipse light is strange and ethereal. Consider using that light to take unique pictures of things and people. It's rare and you may have something no one else does.

PHOTOGRAPHY

FOCAL LENGTH & THE SIZE OF SUN

The size of the sun in a photo depends on the lens focal length. A 300mm lens is the recommended minimum on a full-frame (FF) DSLR. Lenses up to this size are relatively inexpensive. For more magnification, use an APS-C (crop) size sensor. Cameras with these sensors provide an advantage by capturing a larger sun.

For the same focal length, an APS-C sensor will provide a greater apparent magnification of any object. As a consequence, a shorter, less expensive lens can be used to capture the same size sun.

The below figure shows the size of the sun on a camera sensor at various focal lengths. As can be seen with the 200mm lens, the sun is quite small. On a full-frame camera at 200mm, the sun will be 371 pixels wide on a Nikon D810, a 36-megapixel body. A lower resolution FF camera will result in an even smaller sun.

Printing a 24-inch image shot on a Nikon D810 with a 200mm lens at a standard 300 pixels per inch results in a small sun. On this size paper, the sun will be a miserly 1.25 inches wide!

Photographing the eclipse with a lens shorter than 300mm will leave you with little to work with. Using a 400mm lens and printing a 24-inch print will result in a 2.5-inch-wide sun. For as massive as the sun is, it is a challenge to take a large photograph of the sun. The sun will appear to move fast with a 500mm lens, too. Plan to adjust.

PHOTOGRAPHY

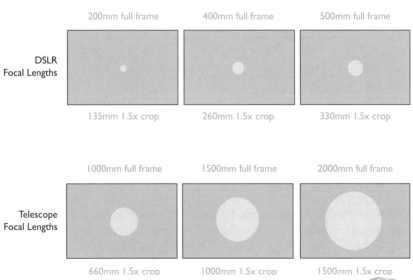

FOCAL LENGTH	FOV FULL FRAME	FF VERT. ANGLE	% OF FF	SUN PIXEL SIZE
14	104° X 81°	81°	0.7%	32.1
20	84° X 62°	62°	0.9%	41.9
28	65° X 46°	46°	1.2%	56.5
35	54° X 38°	38°	1.4%	68.5
50	40° X 27°	27°	2.0%	96.4
105	19° X 13°	13°	4.1%	200.2
200	10° X 7°	7°	7.6%	371.9
400	5° X 3.4°	3.4°	15.6%	765.6
500	4° X 2.7°	2.7°	19.6%	964.2
1000	2° X 1.3°	1.3°	40.8%	2002.5
1500	1.4° X 0.9°	0.9°	58.9%	2892.6
2000	1° X 0.68°	0.68°	77.9%	3828.4

Chart 1: Full-frame camera field of view. The 3rd column is the vertical field of view in degrees. Column 4 is the percentage of the total sensor height that the sun covers. Column 5 is how many pixels wide the sun will be on a 36MP Nikon D810. (Values are estimates)

FOCAL LENGTH	FOV CROP	CROP VERT DEG	% OF CROP	SUN PIXEL SIZE
14	80° X 58°	58°	0.9%	33.9
20	61° X 43°	43°	1.2%	45.8
28	45° X 31°	31°	1.7%	63.5
35	37° X 25°	25°	2.1%	78.7
50	26° X 18°	18°	2.9%	109.3
105	13° X 8°	8°	6.6%	245.9
200	6.7° X 4.5°	4.5°	11.8%	437.2
400	3.4° X 2°	2°	26.5%	983.7
500	2.7° X 1.8	1.8°	29.4%	1093.0
1000	1.3° X 0.9°	0.9°	58.9%	2186.0
1500	0.9° X 0.6°	0.6°	88.3%	3278.9
2000	0.6° X 0.45°	0.5°	117.8%	4371.9

Chart 2: APS-C Crop sensor camera field of view. The 3rd column is the vertical field of view in degrees. Column 4 is the percentage of the total sensor height that the sun covers. Column 5 is how many pixels wide the sun will be on a 12mp Nikon D300s. (Values are estimates)

The big challenge is the cost of the lens. Lenses longer than 300mm are expensive. They also require heavier tripods and specialized tripod heads. The 70-300mm lenses from Nikon, Canon, Tamron, and others are relatively affordable options. It is worth spending time at a local camera shop to try different lenses. Long focal-length lenses are a significant investment, especially for a single event.

To achieve a large eclipse image, you will need a long focal-length lens, ideally at least 400mm. A standard 70-300mm lens set to 300mm will show a small sun. At 500mm, the sun image becomes larger and covers more of the sensor area. The corona will take up a significant portion of the frame. By 1000mm, the corona will exceed the capture area on a full-frame sensor. See the picture in this chapter for sun size simulations for different focal lengths.

SUGGESTED EXPOSURES

To photograph the partial eclipse, the camera must have a solar filter attached. If not, the intense light from the sun may damage (fry) the inside of your camera. This has happened to the author. The exposure depends on the density (darkness) of the solar filter used.

As a starting point, set the camera to ISO 100, f/8, and with the solar filter on, try an exposure of 1/2000. Make adjustments based on the filter used, histogram, and highlight warning.

Turn on the highlight warning in your camera. This feature is commonly called "blinkies." This warning will help you detect if the image is overexposed or not.

Once the Baily's Beads, prominences, and corona become visible, there will only be a few minutes to take bracketed shots. It will take at least eleven shots to capture the various areas of the sun's corona and stars. The brightness varies considerably. No commercially available camera can capture the incredible dynamic range of the different portions of the delicate corona. This requires taking multiple photographs and digitally combining them afterward.

During totality, try these exposure times at ISO 100 and f/8: 1/4000, 1/2000, 1/1000, 1/250, 1/60, 1/30, 1/15, 1/4, 1/2, 1 sec, and 4 sec.

Disable camera/lens stabilization on a tripod!

PHOTOGRAPHY

PHOTOGRAPHY TIME

Set the camera to full-stop adjustments. It will reduce the time spent fiddling. As an example, the author tried the above shot sequence, adjusting the shutter speed as fast as possible.

It took thirty-three seconds to shoot the above 11 shots using 1/3-stop increments. This was without adjusting composition, focus, or anything else but the shutter speed. When the camera was set to full stop increments, it only took twenty-two seconds to step through the same shutter speed sequence. Use a remote release to reduce camera shake.

Assuming the totality lasts less than two minutes, only four shot sequences could be made using 1/3-stop increments. Yet six shot sequences could be made when the camera was set to full stop steps. Zero time was spent looking at the back LCD to analyze highlights and the histogram.

Now add in the bare minimum time to check the highlight warning. It took sixty-three seconds to shoot and check each image using full stops. And that was without changing the composition to allow for sun movement, bumping the tripod, etc. Looking at the LCD ("chimping") consumed **half** of the totality time.

This test was done in the comfort of home under no pressure. In real world conditions, it may be possible to successfully shoot only one sequence. If you plan to capture the entire dynamic range of the totality, you must practice the sequence until you have it down cold. If you normally fumble with your camera, do not underestimate the difficulty, frustration, and stress of total eclipse photography.

Most importantly, trying to shoot this sequence allowed for zero time to simply look at the totality to enjoy the spectacle.

AVOID LAST MINUTE PURCHASES

You should purchase whatever you think you'll need to photograph the eclipse early. This event will be nothing short of massive. Remember the hot toy of the year? Multiply that frenzy by a thousand. Everyone will want to try to capture their own photo.

Do not wait until the last few weeks before the eclipse to purchase cameras, lenses, filters, tripods, viewing glasses, and associated material. Consider that the totality of the eclipse will streak across

America. Everyone who wants to photograph the eclipse will order at the same time. If you wait until too late to buy what you need, it's conceivable that solar filters to create a total eclipse photo will be sold out in the United States. All filters sold out during the 2017 total eclipse. Whether this happens or not, do not wait to make your purchases. It may be too late.

PRACTICE

You will need to practice with your equipment. Things may go wrong that you don't anticipate. If you've never photographed a partial or total eclipse, taking quality shots is more difficult than you think. Practice shooting the sequence with a midday sun. This will tell you if you have your exposures and timing correct. Figure out what you need well in advance.

Practice photographing the full moon and stars at night. Capture the moon in full daylight to learn how your camera reacts. Astrophotography is challenging and requires practice.

PHOTOGRAPHY

The August 21, 2017, eclipse as seen in Jackson, WY, shot with a Nikon D800 with an 80-400mm lens set to 340mm. The sun is 644 pixels wide on the 7360x4912 image.

This image is shown straight out of the camera without modification. Even with a high-quality camera and lens, photographing an eclipse is challenging.

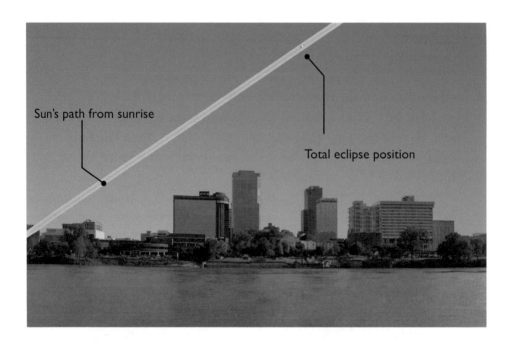

Sun's path from sunrise

Total eclipse position

The eclipse will follow this approximate path on the afternoon of April 8, 2024. Image of downtown Little Rock, AR.

Note that this image is a simulation and approximation the sun's path and where the total eclipse may appear from one perspective. Refer to the eclipse position data for a more accurate location.

LOCATIONS

⊙ is the symbol for the sun and first appeared in Europe during the Renaissance.
☾ is the ancient symbol for the moon.

Viewing Locations Around Arkansas

Tens of thousands of people will travel to and around Arkansas to view the total eclipse. There are few obstructions and there is a vast amount of space to view the total eclipse from.

If the weather is questionable, seek out a new location as soon as possible. If you wait until the hour before the eclipse, you may find yourself stuck in traffic, as others will be looking for a viewing location. Be safe on the roadways, as drivers may be distracted.

This section contains popular, alternative, and little-known locations to watch the eclipse. As long as there are no clouds or smoke from fires, the partial eclipse will be viewable from anywhere in the state.

SUGGESTED TOTAL ECLIPSE VIEW POINTS

TOWNS AND CITIES

- Batesville
- Cabot
- Clarksville
- Clinton
- Conway
- Corning
- De Queen
- Hardy
- Jonesboro
- Little Rock
- Marshall
- Morrilton
- Mountain View
- Newport
- Paragould
- Russellville
- Texarkana

Little Rock

Arkansas Total
Eclipse Path

LOCATIONS

UNIQUE LOCATIONS

- Hot Springs National Park
- Ouachita National Forest
- Ozark National Forest
- Petit Jean State Park

BATESVILLE

Elevation:	362 feet
Population:	10,740
Main road/hwy:	US 167

OVERVIEW

Batesville is located at the shoreline of the White River. The largest city of Independence County is the Ozark region's manufacturing hub and is second to Georgetown as the oldest municipality in Arkansas. Batesville has a wide range of activities that are fun, including camping, social attractions like the Triangle Outdoors LLC, and the Lyon College Holloway Theatre. Catch a movie at the Melba Theater to escape for a few hours. The most popular attraction for car enthusiasts, the Mark Martin Museum, is a must-see, as is the Old Independence Regional Museum for history lovers in Batesville.

GETTING THERE

Drive northeast from Little Rock on US 67 for sixty-one miles, then continue north on US 167 for another thirty-three miles to reach Batesville.

TOTALITY DURATION

4 minutes 2 seconds

NOTES

Visit the city's website for eclipse updates at www.cityofbatesville.com.

Event	Time (CDT)	Altitude	Azimuth
Sunrise	6:42:00AM	0°	80°
Eclipse Start	12:36:07PM	61°	163°
Totality Start	1:53:05PM	60°	202°
Totality End	1:57:08PM	59°	204°
Eclipse End	3:13:16PM	49°	223°
Sunset	7:34:00PM	0°	279°

LOCATIONS

CABOT

Elevation:	295 feet
Population:	25,797
Main road/hwy:	US 167

OVERVIEW

Cabot is a suburb of Little Rock and is the largest city in Lonoke County. The city owes its origin to a small settlement at a refueling station back in the 1880s. It is among the many towns to enjoy the eclipse in Arkansas. Copper Well Retreat is an excellent place to drain off the excitement and stress once the eclipse is over. Cabot is also home to the Cypress Creek Golf Club, gift and specialty shops, studios, and shopping malls. Accommodations and hospitality are available for visitors of most any budget.

GETTING THERE

Drive northwest from Little Rock on US 167 for twenty-six miles to reach Cabot.

TOTALITY DURATION

2 minutes 40 seconds

NOTES

The Cabot city website will have eclipse updates at www.cabotar.gov.

Event	Time (CDT)	Altitude	Azimuth
Sunrise	6:45:00AM	0°	80°
Eclipse Start	12:34:14PM	61°	161°
Totality Start	1:52:08PM	60°	202°
Totality End	1:54:49PM	60°	203°
Eclipse End	3:12:03PM	50°	233°
Sunset	7:35:00PM	0°	279°

LOCATIONS

CLARKSVILLE

Elevation:	364 feet	Clarksville
Population:	9,524	
Main road/hwy:	I-40	

OVERVIEW

Clarksville is located in Johnson County. It is one of the eclipse locations in Arkansas that will experience a totality over three minutes. It is famous for the Johnson County Peach Festival held in July. This is a cultural festival that lasts a week, showcasing arts and crafts, delicacies, grooming, music, pig chases, and many other activities. For social antiques lovers, the Oak General Store is a site to see. Clarksville is also famous for its Post Office mural painted in 1941. Cline Park offers the touch of nature and will be an excellent spot to enjoy the eclipse from. The Clarksville Aquatic Center is a good place to take the kids before or after the eclipse. Visit their website at www.clarksvilleaquaticcenter.com for more details.

GETTING THERE

Drive northwest on I-40 from Little Rock for one hundred and three miles to reach Clarksville.

TOTALITY DURATION

3 minutes 27 seconds

NOTES

The city is located on the Arkansas River.

Event	Time (CDT)	Altitude	Azimuth
Sunrise	6:50:00AM	0°	80°
Eclipse Start	12:32:57PM	60°	158°
Totality Start	1:50:10PM	61°	198°
Totality End	1:53:33PM	60°	199°
Eclipse End	3:10:23PM	51°	230°
Sunset	7:41:00PM	0°	279°

LOCATIONS

CLINTON

Elevation:	559 feet
Population:	2,518
Main road/hwy:	US 65

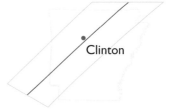

OVERVIEW

Serving as the county seat of Van Buren County, the town of Clinton is an excellent location to view the total eclipse from, as the town nearly sits on the centerline. It is famous for its natural stone bridge formed by water. Archey Fork Park will be a congregating point for eclipse chasers. Clinton has a good selection of three-star hotels, restaurants, and eateries to pick from. Visit the town's website for updated eclipse information at www.clintonark.com. For a unique experience, visit Indian Cave at the Wyndham Resort at Fairfield Bay.

GETTING THERE

Drive north from Little Rock on I-40 until the city of Conway. Then continue north on US 65 to reach Clinton.

TOTALITY DURATION

4 minutes 14 seconds

NOTES

Visit the Archey Fork Park website for eclipse-viewing updates at www.clintonark.com/park.

Event	Time (CDT)	Altitude	Azimuth
Sunrise	6:46:00AM	0°	80°
Eclipse Start	12:34:35PM	60°	161°
Totality Start	1:51:27PM	60°	200°
Totality End	1:55:42PM	60°	202°
Eclipse End	3:11:56PM	50°	231°
Sunset	7:37:00PM	0°	279°

LOCATIONS

Conway

Elevation:	308 feet
Population:	65,300
Main road/hwy:	I-40

Conway

Overview

Conway is in the list of the top twenty eclipse locations in Arkansas. It is the county seat of Faulkner County and also serves as a shopping and cultural hub for the whole Faulkner region. It is the seventh largest city in Arkansas. It is well known for its list of indoor and outdoor amusement activities. One location that stands out is the Cadron Settlement Park where nature comes to life with beauty. On the National Register of Historical Places, the museum shares the experience of the Cherokee Trail of Tears. Hogwild Family Fun Center also provides families with a wholesome experience.

Getting There

Drive north from Little Rock for thirty-two miles on I-40 to reach Conway.

Totality Duration

3 minutes 54 seconds

Notes

Conway's town website will have links to eclipse updates at cityofconway.org.

LOCATIONS

Event	Time (CDT)	Altitude	Azimuth
Sunrise	6:46:00AM	0°	80°
Eclipse Start	12:33:46PM	61°	160°
Totality Start	1:50:59PM	61°	200°
Totality End	1:54:54PM	60°	202°
Eclipse End	3:11:32PM	51°	232°
Sunset	7:36:00PM	0°	279°

CORNING

Elevation:	283 feet
Population:	3,679
Main road/hwy:	US 62

Corning

OVERVIEW

Located in northeast Arkansas, Corning will experience nearly a four-minute totality during the eclipse. The town is located two miles to the west of Black River, which will make an interesting wide-angle composition for the eclipse. The establishment of Corning was started by two brothers, Levi and Solomon Hecht, who ran a lumber mill back in the late 1800s. Corning's economy is primarily based on agriculture, so there is an abundance of clear sky to enjoy the eclipse.

GETTING THERE

Drive north from Paragould for twenty-nine miles on AR-135/US 62 to reach Corning.

TOTALITY DURATION

3 minutes 54 seconds

NOTES

Corning's chamber of commerce will have eclipse updates posted on its website at www.corningar.gov.

LOCATIONS

Event	Time (CDT)	Altitude	Azimuth
Sunrise	6:38:00AM	0°	80°
Eclipse Start	12:38:58PM	60°	167°
Totality Start	1:55:51PM	58°	205°
Totality End	1:59:42PM	58°	207°
Eclipse End	3:15:26PM	48°	234°
Sunset	7:30:00PM	0°	279°

DE QUEEN

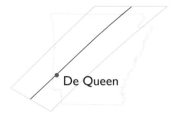

Elevation:	425 feet
Population:	6,565
Main road/hwy:	AR 329

OVERVIEW

Named after the Dutch merchant Jan de Goeijen, De Queen will be an excellent location to view the total eclipse in 2024. De Queen serves as the county seat for Sevier County. The city is backed by rich history from the Dutch. The town has multiple motels and hotels to choose from. Make sure to book early. Once word of the eclipse spreads, room availability will drop and prices will increase. Delicacies served at the selected restaurants like Stilwell's, the Ranch House Café, and others will top your experience.

GETTING THERE

Drive north from Texarkana on US 71 for forty miles, then turn northwest on AR 329 and drive for twelve miles to reach De Queen.

TOTALITY DURATION

4 minutes 17 seconds

NOTES

De Queen's website is cityofdequeen.com. Check for eclipse updates.

Event	Time (CDT)	Altitude	Azimuth
Sunrise	6:55:00AM	0°	80°
Eclipse Start	12:29:05PM	61°	153°
Totality Start	1:46:16PM	62°	194°
Totality End	1:50:34PM	62°	197°
Eclipse End	3:07:43PM	53°	229°
Sunset	7:43:00PM	0°	279°

LOCATIONS

HARDY

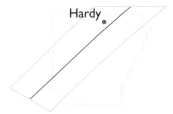
Hardy

Elevation:	376 feet
Population:	769
Main road/hwy:	US 412

OVERVIEW

Hardy is located in Sharp and Fulton Counties. The town supports several gift shops and a fascinating collection of classic cars at the Vintage Motorcar Museum at 301 W. Main Street. Visit the Veterans Military Museum to see a tribute to America's armed forces. Griffin Park will be a good location to set up an eclipse-viewing event for your family or group. Make sure to secure your event permit from the town well in advance of the eclipse.

GETTING THERE

Drive northwest from Jonesboro on US 63 and continue on US 412 for sixty-two miles to reach Hardy.

TOTALITY DURATION

4 minutes 12 seconds

NOTES

Note that Hardy may struggle with the expected number of visitors for the eclipse. Be prepared with extra supplies.

LOCATIONS

Event	Time (CDT)	Altitude	Azimuth
Sunrise	6:41:00AM	0°	80°
Eclipse Start	12:37:15PM	60°	164°
Totality Start	1:53:57PM	59°	203°
Totality End	1:58:09PM	59°	205°
Eclipse End	3:13:56PM	49°	232°
Sunset	7:34:00PM	0°	279°

JONESBORO

Elevation:	322 feet
Population:	74,889
Main road/hwy:	AR 226

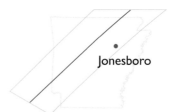

Jonesboro

OVERVIEW

Jonesboro is among the many Arkansas eclipse cities that will give you value for your visit. It is the fifth most populous city in Arkansas. Jonesboro is home to Arkansas State University, the ASU Art Museum, and the Centennial Bank Stadium. Should you want to fish before or after the eclipse, Craighead Forest Park is an excellent choice. The lake will be a good place to view the eclipse. The shopping mall at Turtle Creek provides its visitors with a wide range of items. Stores in the mall will have eclipse-related products to enhance your experience. There is even a bowling alley should you want to escape for a few hours.

GETTING THERE

Drive northeast from Little Rock on US 67, then continue on AR 226 for one hundred thirty-one miles to reach Jonesboro.

TOTALITY DURATION

2 minutes 28 seconds

NOTES

The Jonesboro website will have eclipse updates in early 2024 at www.jonesboro.org.

LOCATIONS

Event	Time (CDT)	Altitude	Azimuth
Sunrise	6:39:00AM	0°	80°
Eclipse Start	12:37:41PM	61°	166°
Totality Start	1:55:28PM	59°	205°
Totality End	1:57:56PM	59°	206°
Eclipse End	3:14:39PM	49°	234°
Sunset	7:30:00PM	0°	279°

LITTLE ROCK

Elevation:	335 feet	
Population:	198,491	
Main road/hwy:	Multiple	

Little Rock

OVERVIEW

Located on the Arkansas River, Little Rock, the state's capital, has much to pride itself on. As one of the few state capitals under the totality, Little Rock will be a unique location to view the eclipse from. Visit the Old Statehouse Museum and the Central High Museum to get a flavor of the state. Little Rock is a host to a range of mouthwatering eateries where visitors can get a taste of glamorous delicacies. Try out Brave New Restaurant, Table 28, or Sonny Williams Steak Room for a romantic bite. Little Rock also provides its visitors with a thrilling experience while shopping at the River Market District. Visit their website at www.rivermarket.info.

GETTING THERE

Little Rock is Arkansas's capital and can be reached by plane, car, or bus.

TOTALITY DURATION

2 minutes 31 seconds

NOTES

Visit the Museum of Discovery website at www.museumofdiscovery. org for updated eclipse education information.

Event	Time (CDT)	Altitude	Azimuth
Sunrise	6:46:00AM	0°	80°
Eclipse Start	12:33:25PM	61°	160°
Totality Start	1:51:29PM	61°	201°
Totality End	1:54:07PM	61°	202°
Eclipse End	3:11:29PM	61°	232°
Sunset	7:35:00PM	0°	279°

LOCATIONS

MARSHALL

Elevation:	1,040 feet	
Population:	1,355	
Main road/hwy:	US 65	

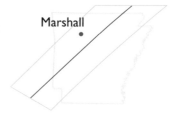

OVERVIEW

Originally known as Burrowsville, Marshall owes the origin of its name to the United States Supreme Court Chief Justice John Marshall. If you are feeling nostalgic, visit the Kenda Drive-In movie theater. Visit their website at www.kendadrivein.com. Marshall is an excellent jumping-off point for outdoor adventure activities like camping at the Tyler Bend Campground in the Buffalo National River run by the National Park Service. Established as America's first National River, this is a unique location to view the eclipse from. The park is ten miles from the river on US 65.

GETTING THERE

Drive twenty-seven miles north on US 65 from Clinton to Marshall.

TOTALITY DURATION

3 minutes 48 seconds

NOTES

As with the 2017 eclipse, the national parks along the totality path were heavily impacted. Make reservations well in advance to ensure that your plans will be successful. Visit the park's website for contact information at www.nps.gov/buff.

Event	Time (CDT)	Altitude	Azimuth
Sunrise	6:47:00AM	0°	80°
Eclipse Start	12:34:52PM	60°	160°
Totality Start	1:51:49PM	60°	200°
Totality End	1:55:37PM	60°	201°
Eclipse End	3:11:57PM	50°	231°
Sunset	7:38:00PM	0°	279°

LOCATIONS

MORRILTON

Elevation:	387 feet
Population:	6,722
Main road/hwy:	US 64

Morrilton

OVERVIEW

Located nearly fifty miles from Little Rock, Morrilton is located in Conway County in Arkansas. Cedar Falls Trail is an excellent site to enjoy a walk in nature and experience one of the most beautiful celestial phenomena known. Specialty museums like the Museum of Automobiles will also add value to your leisure time. Visit their website at www.museumofautos.com. Barnyard Friend and Stables has a petting zoo and gives you the opportunity to view and learn about animals. Should you be a lover of wine, Movie House Winery does it all. Their website is www.moviehousewinery.com.

GETTING THERE

Drive west from Conway on I-40 for twelve miles, then continue on US 64 for six miles to reach Morrilton.

TOTALITY DURATION

4 minutes 13 seconds

NOTES

Make reservations early in Morrilton for any lodging you may need.

Event	Time (CDT)	Altitude	Azimuth
Sunrise	6:48:00AM	0°	80°
Eclipse Start	12:33:25PM	61°	159°
Totality Start	1:50:26PM	61°	199°
Totality End	1:54:39PM	60°	201°
Eclipse End	3:11:09PM	51°	231°
Sunset	7:38:00PM	0°	279°

Mountain View

Elevation:	761 feet
Population:	2,860
Main road/hwy:	AR 14

Mountain View

Overview

Mountain View is yet another location to consider to watch the eclipse in Arkansas. It is known for the Blanchard Springs Caverns that offer a thrilling experience for its visitors. Adventurous people will find this site amazing and fun. The Ozark Folk Center State Park also provides a wholesome experience with its calm and serene nature. The Blanchard Springs Recreation area is best for meditation and reflection on the eclipse. For history buffs, The Old Mill ruins at the Blanchard Springs Caverns and the Peace Pole are well worth a visit. It may make for a unique total eclipse photograph. For theater fans, the White River Theater is an excellent choice for entertainment.

Getting There

Drive west on AR 14 for thirty-eight miles from Batesville to reach Mountain View.

Totality Duration

4 minutes 13 seconds

Notes

Visit the Mountain View Chamber of Commerce website for eclipse updates at www.yourplaceinthemountains.com.

Event	Time (CDT)	Altitude	Azimuth
Sunrise	6:44:00AM	0°	80°
Eclipse Start	12:35:34PM	60°	162°
Totality Start	1:52:22PM	60°	201°
Totality End	1:56:35PM	59°	203°
Eclipse End	3:12:40PM	50°	232°
Sunset	7:36:00PM	0°	279°

Newport

Elevation:	224 feet	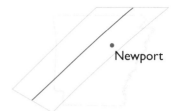
Population:	7,897	
Main road/hwy:	US 67	

Overview

Newport is located on the White River. As one of the many cities along the eclipse path, Newport is graced by the Iron Mountain Depot dating from 1902. There is a museum on the location dedicated to this old train depot. In fact, the city hosts Depot Days during the summer. The town has a nightlife with an assortment of bars and restaurants to suit your style. Make sure to set your reservations early at any of the hotels and motels so you have some place to stay during the eclipse.

Getting There

Drive northeast from Little Rock for ninety-one miles on US 167/67 to reach Newport.

Totality Duration

3 minutes 8 seconds

Notes

The city of Newport will likely have eclipse updates on their official website in 2024 at www.newportarcity.org.

Event	Time (CDT)	Altitude	Azimuth
Sunrise	6:41:00AM	0°	80°
Eclipse Start	12:36:24PM	61°	164°
Totality Start	1:53:54PM	60°	203°
Totality End	1:57:03PM	59°	205°
Eclipse End	3:13:39PM	49°	223°
Sunset	7:32:00PM	0°	279°

LOCATIONS

PARAGOULD

Elevation: 304 feet
Population: 28,232
Main road/hwy: US 49

OVERVIEW

Paragould is one of the larger cities in Arkansas that will enjoy the total eclipse on April 8, 2024. It is home to several state parks including the notable Crowley's Ridge State Park which features fishing boat, kayak, and pedal boat rentals. The city is home to unique restaurants like Roy's First and Last Chance, a unique Arkansas experience. The Paragould War Memorial features a scaled-down version of the Statue of Liberty in Courthouse Park. This may make an interesting total eclipse composition, as the original statue in New York won't see a total eclipse until 2079.

GETTING THERE

Drive northeast from Jonesboro on US 49 for twenty-one miles to reach Paragould.

TOTALITY DURATION

2 minutes 50 seconds

NOTES

Check the Paragould city website for eclipse updates at www.paragould.org.

Event	Time (CDT)	Altitude	Azimuth
Sunrise	6:38:00AM	0°	80°
Eclipse Start	12:38:21PM	60°	167°
Totality Start	1:55:52PM	59°	205°
Totality End	1:58:42PM	58°	207°
Eclipse End	3:15:07PM	48°	234°
Sunset	7:29:00PM	0°	279°

LOCATIONS

RUSSELLVILLE

Elevation:	341 feet
Population:	27,583
Main road/hwy:	I-40

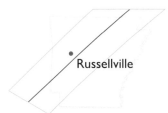

OVERVIEW

Russellville is the county seat of Pope County. It has a variety of fun outdoor activities to engage in while spending time there that include adventures like hiking, swimming, camping, and fishing, owing to its large bodies of water in the Ozark-St. Francis National Forest. If you are certified, hang glide and paraglide from Mount Nebo just outside the city. The city is also home to Arkansas Tech University and Arkansas Nuclear One, the state's only nuclear power facility. Don't worry—the total eclipse will not affect the reactor in any way. It's just a shadow.

GETTING THERE

Drive northwest from Little Rock on I-40 for seventy-seven miles to reach Russellville.

TOTALITY DURATION

4 minutes 10 seconds

NOTES

Visit the Russellville website for eclipse, travel, and lodging updates at www.russellvillearkansas.org.

Event	Time (CDT)	Altitude	Azimuth
Sunrise	6:48:00AM	0°	80°
Eclipse Start	12:33:03PM	60°	158°
Totality Start	1:49:59PM	61°	198°
Totality End	1:54:10PM	60°	200°
Eclipse End	3:10:41PM	51°	230°
Sunset	7:40:00PM	0°	279°

LOCATIONS

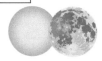

Texarkana

Elevation:	363 feet
Population:	30,283
Main road/hwy:	I-30

Overview

Situated on the border of Arkansas and Texas, Texarkana is home to multiple museums that will be of interest when visiting for the total eclipse. These include the Texarkana Museum of Regional History, Discovery Place Children's Museum, the Four States Auto Museum, Ace of Clubs House, and the Lindsey Railroad Museum. Holiday Springs Water Park is another of Texarkana's unique attractions. The water park has a numerous number of slides for kids and adults. Bobby Ferguson Park offers a serene outdoor experience for both couples and people who love spending quality time outdoors. The Arkansas Convention Center together with the city market offers visitors a wide range of products to purchase eclipse souvenirs.

Getting There

Drive southwest from Little Rock on I-30 for one hundred forty-three miles to reach Texarkana.

Totality Duration

2 minutes 30 seconds

Notes

The Texarkana city website is arkansas.txkusa.org.

Event	Time (CDT)	Altitude	Azimuth
Sunrise	6:54:00AM	0°	80°
Eclipse Start	12:28:30PM	61°	153°
Totality Start	1:46:48PM	63°	196°
Totality End	1:49:19PM	63°	197°
Eclipse End	3:07:34PM	53°	230°
Sunset	7:41:00PM	0°	279°

LOCATIONS

HOT SPRINGS NATIONAL PARK

Elevation: 892 feet
Main road/hwy: US 70

Hot Springs
National Park

OVERVIEW

This national park located in Garland County, Arkansas, is one of few National Park Service locations to view the eclipse from. It is best known for the natural hot springs that it derives its name from. Nicknamed "The American Spa," this park features multiple bathhouses that people came to "take the waters" for health and relaxation. This park offers a wholesome experience for both visitors and locals enjoying various activities at the park. The historic Fordyce Bathhouse, built in 1910, houses a visitor center to help you better appreciate the location. The Grand Promenade is a centerpiece of the park and worth visiting. The nearby Gangster Museum of America is worth a visit to add to the experience too.

GETTING THERE

Drive southwest from Little Rock on I-30 and exit on US 70 to reach the park.

TOTALITY DURATION

3 minutes 42 seconds

NOTES

Refer to the park's website for updates at www.nps.gov/hosp.

Event	Time (CDT)	Altitude	Azimuth
Sunrise	6:49:00AM	0°	80°
Eclipse Start	12:31:52PM	61°	157°
Totality Start	1:49:20PM	61°	198°
Totality End	1:53:02PM	61°	200°
Eclipse End	3:10:06PM	52°	231°
Sunset	7:38:00PM	0°	279°

LOCATIONS

OUACHITA NATIONAL FOREST

Elevation:	Varies	
Main road/hwy:	Multiple	

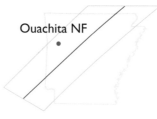

Ouachita NF

OVERVIEW

Ouachita National Forest is located between western Arkansas and eastern Oklahoma. Roughly two-thirds of the central and eastern part of the forest will experience the total eclipse. It has a number of sites for people to view and engage in activities. Beavers Bend Resort Park is an excellent camping site. Lake Ouachita, Broken Bow Lake, and Talimena Scenic Drive are all beautiful venues to view and photograph the eclipse from.

GETTING THERE

The Ouachita NF can be accessed from multiple locations in Arkansas. Hot Springs is a good starting point to access the forest.

TOTALITY DURATION

Multiple depending on location.

NOTES

Visit the forest's website at www.fs.usda.gov/ouachita for eclipse updates at the event draws closer.

LOCATIONS

Times are for the town of Oden.

Event	Time (CDT)	Altitude	Azimuth
Sunrise	6:52:00AM	0°	80°
Eclipse Start	12:30:57PM	61°	156°
Totality Start	1:48:00PM	62°	196°
Totality End	1:52:18PM	61°	199°
Eclipse End	3:09:08PM	52°	230°
Sunset	7:41:00PM	0°	279°

Ozark National Forest

Elevation:	Varies	
Main road/hwy:	Multiple	

Overview

The Ozark National Forest is another Arkansas natural location to enjoy the total eclipse from. The excellent natural scenery is a great destination for camping lovers. The forest has several unique locations like the Lost Valley Hike and Cave. This lost valley has so many wonders to explore. The trail head is located a few miles west of Ponca on Highway 43. Sam's Throne is a popular climbing location for vertically oriented people. Depending on your skill, you may be able to make a unique climbing photograph similar to the viral Smith Rock total eclipse image made in Oregon in 2017. Reach Pam's Grotto Waterfall by hiking a 0.7-mile trail and be rewarded with a gorgeous waterfall spilling out of the rocks.

Getting There

Start at Russellville and drive north to reach the forest.

Totality Duration

Multiple depending on location.

Notes

The western portion of the forest is *outside* the totality.

Times are for the town of Sand Gap.

Event	Time (CDT)	Altitude	Azimuth
Sunrise	6:49:00AM	0°	80°
Eclipse Start	12:33:52PM	60°	159°
Totality Start	1:50:59PM	60°	198°
Totality End	1:54:28PM	60°	200°
Eclipse End	3:11:06PM	51°	230°
Sunset	7:39:00PM	0°	279°

LOCATIONS

Petit Jean State Park

Elevation:	897 feet
Main road/hwy:	AR 154

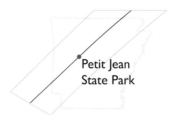

Petit Jean
State Park

Overview

Petit Jean State Park located on the Petit Jean Mountain is a nature-lover's location to view the eclipse from. This 3,471-acre unique landscape inspired the creation of Arkansas's first state park. Petit Jean Mountain rises 1,100 feet above the Arkansas River Valley and will be a prime location to watch the eclipse. There are campsites, waterfalls, and wildlife to enjoy. Visit historic Mather Lodge to develop a sense of the location. Nearby Holla Bend National Wildlife Refuge is a perfect location to observe the effects of a total eclipse on wildlife. Their reaction to the rapid onset of darkness is fascinating and worth watching.

Getting There

Drive south from Morrilton on AR 9, then turn east at Oppelo on AR 154 to reach Petit Jean State Park.

Totality Duration

4 minutes 15 seconds

Notes

Visit the Petit Jean Park website for updated eclipse information at www.petitjeanstatepark.com.

Event	Time (CDT)	Altitude	Azimuth
Sunrise	6:48:00AM	0°	80°
Eclipse Start	12:33:06PM	60°	159°
Totality Start	1:50:06PM	61°	199°
Totality End	1:54:21PM	60°	201°
Eclipse End	3:10:52PM	51°	231°
Sunset	7:38:00PM	0°	279°

REMEMBER THE ARKANSAS TOTAL ECLIPSE
April 8, 2024

Who was I with? _____
_____
_____
_____
_____

What did I see? _____
_____
_____
_____
_____
_____
_____
_____
_____

What did I feel? _____
_____
_____
_____
_____
_____
_____

_____

_____

_____

_____

_____

What did the people with me think? _____

_____

_____

_____

_____

_____

_____

_____

_____

_____

Where did I stay?_____

_____

_____

_____

_____

_____

_____

_____

_____

Enjoy Other Books by Aaron Linsdau

50 Jackson Hole Photography Hotspots

This guide reveals the best Jackson Hole photography spots. Learn what locals and insiders know to find the most impressive and iconic photography locations in the United States. This is an excellent companion guide to the *Jackson Hole Hiking Guide*.
www.sastrugipress.com/books/50-jackson-hole-photography-hotspots/

Adventure Expedition One
by Aaron Linsdau M.S. & Terry Williams, M.D.

Create, finance, enjoy, and return safely from your first expedition. Learn the techniques explorers use to achieve their goals and have a good time doing it. Acquire the skills, find the equipment, learn to camp, understand medical issues, and learn the planning necessary to pull off an expedition.
www.sastrugipress.com/books/adventure-expedition-one/

Antarctic Tears

Experience the honest story of solo polar exploration. This inspirational true book will make readers both cheer and cry. Coughing up blood and fighting skin-freezing temperatures were only a few of the perils Aaron Linsdau faced. Travel with him on a world-record expedition to the South Pole.
www.sastrugipress.com/books/antarctic-tears/

How to Keep Your Feet Warm in the Cold

Keep your feet warm in cold conditions on chilly adventures with techniques described in this book. Packed with dozens and dozens of ideas, learn how to avoid having cold feet ever again in your outdoor pursuits.
www.sastrugipress.com/books/how-to-keep-your-feet-warm-in-the-cold/

Jackson Hole Hiking Guide

Jackson Hole contains some of the most dramatic and iconic landscapes in the United States. The book shares everything you need to know to hike Jackson's classic trails with canyons, high mountains, and hidden alpine lakes. This book is an excellent companion guide to *50 Jackson Hole Photography Hotspots*.
www.sastrugipress.com/books/jackson-hole-hiking-guide/

Subscribe to Aaron's YouTube channel at www.youtube.com/@alinsdau

If you enjoyed this book, please consider leaving a five-star review and a few words on what you liked about it at your favorite online retailer.

Lost at Windy Corner

Windy Corner on Denali has claimed fingers, toes, and even lives. What would make someone brave lethal weather, crevasses, and avalanches to attempt to summit North America's highest mountain? Aaron Linsdau shares the experience of climbing Denali alone and how you can apply the lessons to your life.
www.sastrugipress.com/books/lost-windy-corner/

The Motivated Amateur's Guide to Winter Camping

Winter camping is one of the most satisfying ways to experience the wilderness. It is also the most challenging style of overnighting in the outdoors. Learn 100+ tips from a professional polar explorer on how to winter camp safely and be comfortable in the cold.
www.sastrugipress.com/books/the-motivated-amateurs-guide-to-winter-camping/

Two Friends and a Polar Bear
by Terry Williams, M.D. & Aaron Linsdau

This story of friendship is about two old friends who plan to ski across the Greenland Ice Cap along the Arctic Circle in hopes of becoming one of the oldest teams to succeed.
www.sastrugipress.com/books/two-friends-and-a-polar-bear/

About the Author

Aaron Linsdau is the second American to ski alone from the coast of Antarctica to the South Pole (730 miles / 1174 km), setting a world record for surviving the longest expedition ever for that trip. He lead a 310-mile (499 km) ski expedition across the Greenland icecap along the Arctic Circle. Aaron has climbed Denali solo, crossed the Greenland tundra alone, skied across Yellowstone National Park solo, trekked through the Sahara desert, and successfully climbed Mt. Kilimanjaro and Mt. Elbrus in Russia.

Aaron Linsdau at the South Pole.

Use your smart device to scan the QR codes for website links.

Visit www.aaronlinsdau.com/subscribe to learn more about the author. Receive updates when he releases new books and shows.

Visit Sastrugi Press on the web at www.sastrugipress.com to purchase the above titles in bulk. They are available in print, e-book, or audiobook form.

Thank you for choosing Sastrugi Press.

Enjoy Other Books by Sastrugi Press

50 Florida Wildlife Hotspots by Moose Henderson Ph.D.

This is a definitive guide to finding where to photograph wildlife in Florida. Follow the guidance of a professional wildlife photographer as he takes you to some of the best places to see wildlife in the Sunshine State.

www.sastrugipress.com/books/50-florida-wildlife-hotspots/

50 Wildlife Hotspots Grand Teton National Park by Moose Henderson Ph.D.

Find out where to find animals and photograph them in Grand Teton National Park from a professional wildlife photographer. Learn techniques, timing, animal behavior, and composition to create stunning wildlife images.

www.sastrugipress.com/books/50-wildlife-hotspots/

Alaska: A Guide for the Curious by Nikki Mann & Jeff Wohl

Discover the natural world of Alaska. Find out what the plants and animals are like, how to identify them, and what the environment of Alaska is like.

www.sastrugipress.com/books/alaska-a-guide-for-the-curious/

Blood Justice by Tim W. James

Two brothers, one a preacher's son, the other an adopted would-be slave, set out in opposite directions to avenge their family's murder only to cross paths in pursuit of the killer. Book 1 of the Roger Brinkman Series.

www.sastrugipress.com/iron-spike-press/blood-justice/

Shake Yourself Free by Bob Millsap

Learn how to overcome difficult encounters with misfortune, tragedy, and loss. Emotional recovery is a journey requiring a mindset shift. Get this book now and take control of your life.

www.sastrugipress.com/books/shake-yourself-free/

The Burqa Cave by Dean Petersen

Still haunted by Iraq, a retired soldier seeks solace teaching high school in Wyoming. He soon finds the quiet town is home to murderers, maniacs, and a boy who can see where missing murder victims are. This paranormal thriller-romance surprises readers with unexpected twists.

www.sastrugipress.com/books/the-burqa-cave/

PHOTOGRAPHY NOTES

April 8, 2024

Settings _____

_____

_____

_____

_____

Successes _____

_____

_____

_____

_____

_____

_____

_____

Challenges _____

_____

_____

_____

_____

_____

_____

Photography Notes

April 8, 2024

Camera _____

_____

_____

_____

_____

Company _____

_____

_____

_____

_____

_____

_____

_____

Location _____

_____

_____

_____

_____

_____

_____

Made in United States
Troutdale, OR
01/28/2024

17240116R00042